1

Hand

Piano

Kenneth Baker's
new three-book
piano course

Wise Publications
London/New York/Paris/Sydney/Copenhagen/Madrid

CW00377231

Exclusive Distributors:
Music Sales Limited
8/9 Frith Street,
London W1V 5TZ, England.
Music Sales Pty Limited
120 Rothschild Avenue,
Rosebery, NSW 2018,
Australia.

Order No. AM927520
ISBN 0-7119-4985-9
This book © Copyright 1995 by Wise Publications

Music arranged by Kenneth Baker
Music processed by MSS Studios
Book design by Studio Twenty, London
Cover photograph by George Taylor

Printed in the United Kingdom by
Printwise (Haverhill) Limited, Haverhill, Suffolk.

Your Guarantee of Quality

As publishers, we strive to produce every book to the
highest commercial standards.
The music has been freshly engraved and the book has
been carefully designed to minimise awkward page turns
and to make playing from it a real pleasure.
Particular care has been given to specifying acid-free,
neutral-sized paper made from pulps which have not
been elemental chlorine bleached. This pulp is from
farmed sustainable forests and was produced with
special regard for the environment.
Throughout, the printing and binding have been
planned to ensure a sturdy, attractive publication
which should give years of enjoyment.
If your copy fails to meet our high standards,
please inform us and we will gladly replace it.

Music Sales' complete catalogue describes thousands
of titles and is available in full colour sections by subject,
direct from Music Sales Limited.
Please state your areas of interest and send a
cheque/postal order for £1.50 for postage to:
Music Sales Limited, Newmarket Road,
Bury St. Edmunds, Suffolk IP33 3YB.

About this book

This popular-style piano course is designed specifically for two types of pianist...

1 The player who has some facility in the right hand, but who has a limited left hand technique, and little or no knowledge of bass clef.

2 The totally new pianist who hasn't much time for practice, and simply wants to 'knock out a tune' as quickly as possible.

Although the books stand perfectly well on their own, the following excellent audio 'aids' are available...

CD, cassette and Midi file disk

With any of these aids you can...

Hear how every song should be played

Play along with a full backing band

In addition, with the Midi file disk you can slow down or speed up the tracks as desired, and listen to different parts of the performance (for example, left hand alone, right hand alone, and so on). You will find these audio facilities an enormous advantage when learning to play the piano from these books.

About the audio

Lead-in clicks and intros

On each of the audios there are a number of lead-in 'clicks' (cymbal beats) at the beginning of every track in order to set the speed. There are four clicks with 4/4 Time, three clicks with 3/4 Time, and so on. On some of the tracks these lead-in clicks are followed by a short musical 'introduction' from the backing band. You start playing when you hear the solo piano on the backing track begin.

Note-finding exercises

'Note Finder 1' consists of a musical backing track which will help you practise finding the notes C, D, and E. After eight lead-in cymbal beats from the track, play C notes at random - anywhere you like on the keyboard, up or down - until you hear a loud cymbal crash from the band. At that point change to D notes and continue with these until the next cymbal crash. Now change to E notes and continue similarly to the end of the exercise.

Reset 'Note Finder 1' and repeat as often as necessary until you can pick out all the Cs, Ds and Es on your piano keyboard with ease.

Now move on to 'Note Finder 2' and practise finding the notes F, G, A and B.

Before you start to play...

YOUR POSITION AT THE PIANO

Place the cardboard **Keyboard Guide** which comes with this book behind the keys on your piano, and check that the guide is in the centre of the instrument. Sit relaxed, facing MIDDLE C.

LAYOUT OF THE KEYBOARD

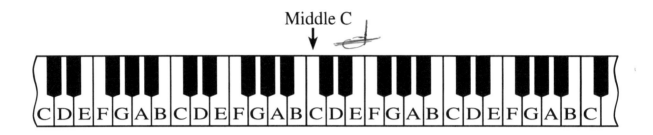

There are only seven different letter names used in music: A, B, C, D, E, F, G. These seven notes repeat over and over again, progressing from the lowest sounds on the left to the highest sounds on the right.
To locate the white notes, use the black note groups:

C lies to the LEFT of every group of TWO black keys.
B lies to the RIGHT of every group of THREE black keys, and so on.

If you have an audio facility, use NOTEFINDER 1 to help you find C, D and E, and NOTEFINDER 2 to help you find F, G, A and B.

FINGER NUMBERS

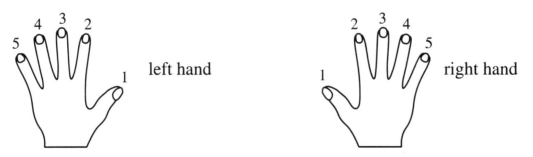

Your right hand plays the 'melody' of each song, using STANDARD MUSICAL NOTATION. Your left hand plays an accompaniment to each song, using CHORD SYMBOLS (though actual notation in the Bass Clef is included for reference).

THE WRITTEN NOTES

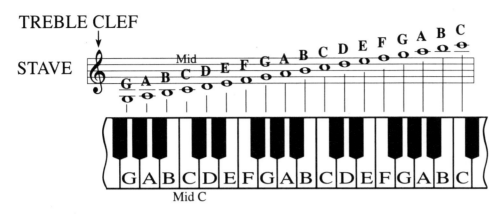

TREBLE CLEF

STAVE

MUSICAL TIMING

Note	Name	Equivalent 'rest'	Duration
♩ or ♩	Quarter Note (Crotchet)	𝄽	1 beat
♩ or ♩	Half Note (Minim)	𝄼	2 beats
♩. or ♩.	Dotted Half Note (Dotted Minim)	𝄼·	3 beats
o	Whole Note (Semibreve)	𝄻	4 beats (or one whole bar)
♪ or ♪ or ♫	Eighth Note (Quaver)	𝄾	½ beat (♫ = ♩)
♬ or ♬ or ♬	Sixteenth Note (Semiquaver)	𝄿	¼ beat (♬♬ = ♩)

DOTTED NOTES.   A dot after a note increases its length by one half:-

♩ = 1 beat   ♩· = 1½ beats

TIE.   ♩‿♩   A curved line joining two notes of the same pitch.
Hold the first note down for the length of both notes.

SEMITONE   The smallest possible distance between notes (white or black)
on a piano keyboard.

SHARPS, FLATS, AND NATURALS

SHARP   ♯   Play the note one semitone to the RIGHT of the marked note.
FLAT   ♭   Play the note one semitone to the LEFT of the marked note.
NATURAL   ♮   Cancel a sharp or flat.

Sharps, flats, and naturals, once written, continue right through their bar.
At the next bar, however, everything returns to normal.

LEGATO   Unmarked, or: ♩ ♩ ♩ ♩   play in a 'joined up' fashion, leaving no
gaps between notes, nor making any ugly overlaps.

STACCATO ♩ ♩ ♩ ♩   Cut the note(s) short.

Learn while you play...

TRIADS

A TRIAD is a three note chord with the following spacing:

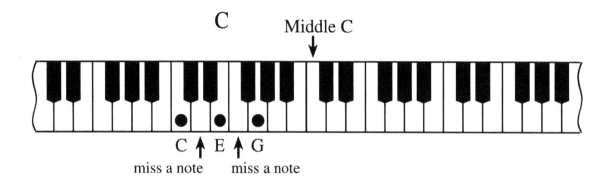

A triad takes its name from its BOTTOM NOTE, so the above chord is called C.

Here are F and G triads:

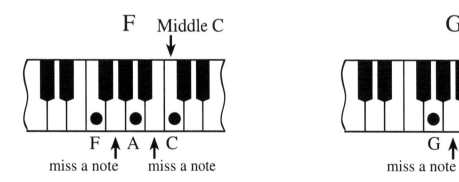

On the piano, triads can be used to create simple but effective left hand accompaniments. The fingering is always the same:

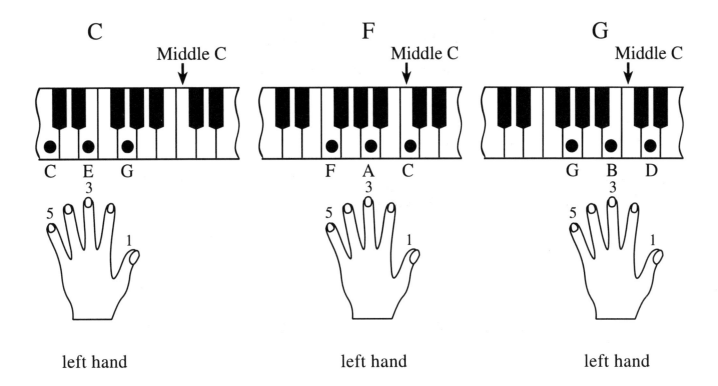

TO FIND A TRIAD

With your left hand little finger (finger 5), point to the chord name you want and adjust your fingers to the correct spacing.

Eight Days A Week

Words & Music by John Lennon & Paul McCartney

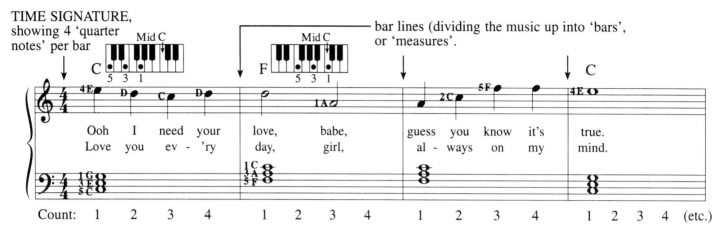

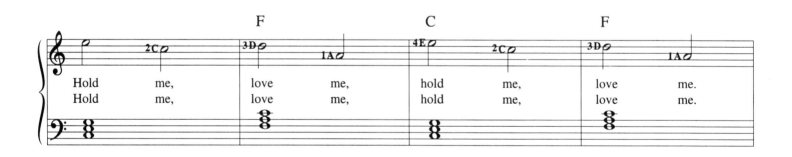

One More Night

Words & Music by Phil Collins

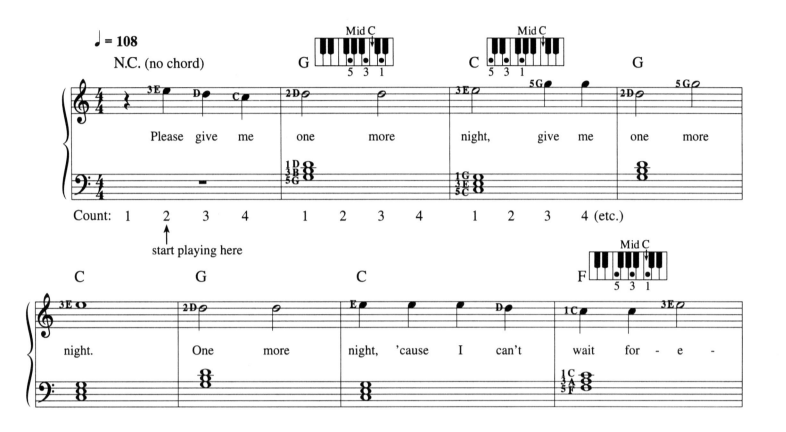

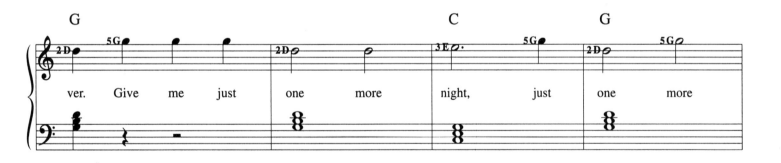

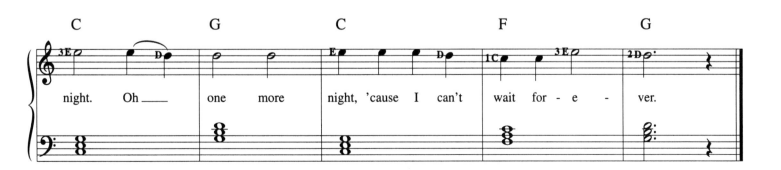

Tales Of The Unexpected (Theme)

Composed by Ron Grainer

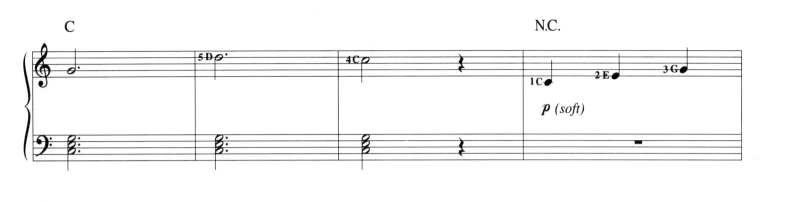

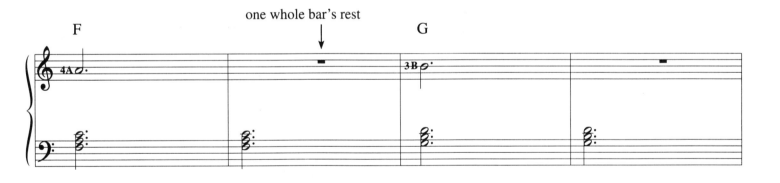

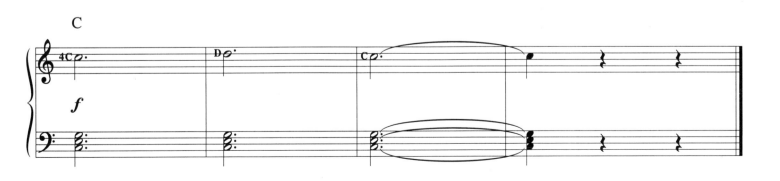

11

Wooden Heart

Words & Music by Fred Wise, Ben Weisman,
Kay Twomey & Berthold Kaempfert

PICK-UP NOTES   Preliminary notes coming before the first beat of the bar. The beats missing from the pick-up bar can usually be found at the end of the piece so that the player can go around again without disturbing the rhythm.

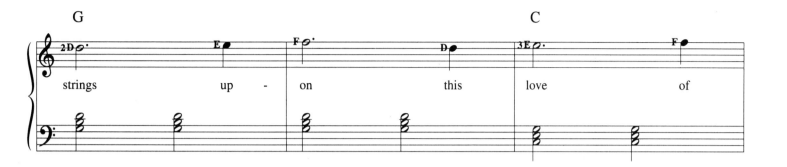

strings   up - on   this   love   of

mine,   it   was   al - ways   you   from   the

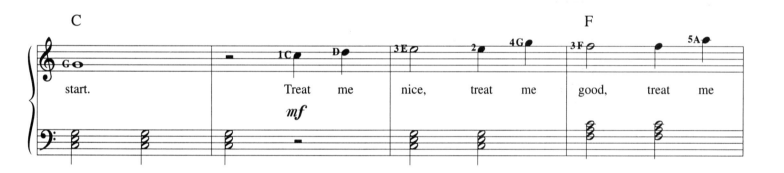

start.   Treat   me   nice,   treat   me   good,   treat   me

mf

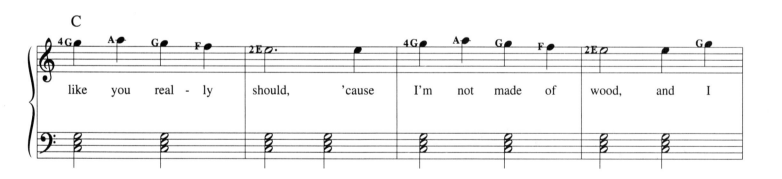

like   you   real - ly   should,   'cause   I'm   not   made   of   wood,   and   I

TIE. Hold this note for 6 beats in all.

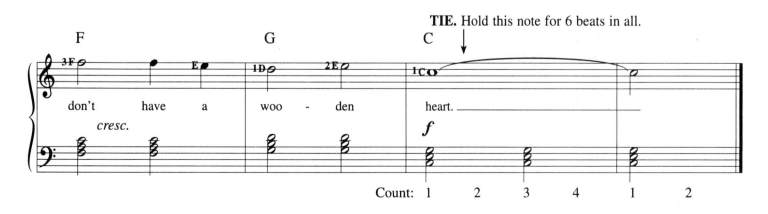

don't   have   a   woo - den   heart. _____

cresc.   *f*

Count: 1   2   3   4   1   2

13

Massachusetts

Words & Music by Barry Gibb, Robin Gibb & Maurice Gibb

* Keep your main beats (1,2,3,4) rock steady, and play your 'and' note ("G") exactly between beats 2 and 3.

Release Me

Words & Music by Eddie Miller,
Dub Williams, Robert Yount & Robert Harris

getting gradually softer

La Bamba

Adapted & Arranged by Ritchie Valens

* VERSE: That part of the song taken (usually) by a solo singer.

* CHORUS: That part of the song where everybody joins in.

MINOR TRIADS

The triads you have used up to now: C, F, and G, are called Major triads.
Minor triads have the same spacing as the Majors, but there is a slight
difference in the position of the middle note. In the Minor triad the middle note
is ONE SEMITONE FURTHER TO THE LEFT:-

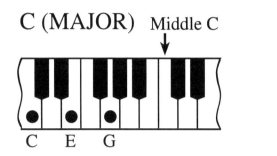 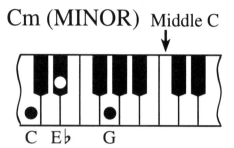

To play the next few songs you need three new MINOR TRIADS.
They consist of all white notes:-

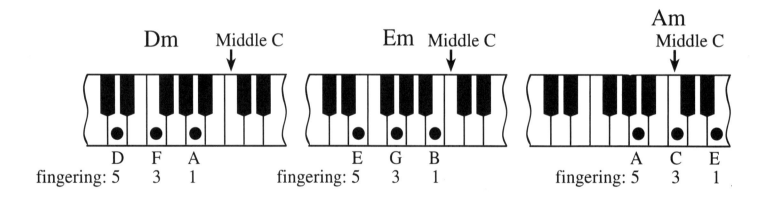

Before you start on the songs, practise the following chord sequence
(up and down the keyboard):-

C   Dm   Em   F   G   Am

Use left hand fingers 5,3,1 throughout, and call out the name of each
chord as you play it.

The Sound Of Silence

Words & Music by Paul Simon

Top Of The World

Words by John Bettis.
Music by Richard Carpenter

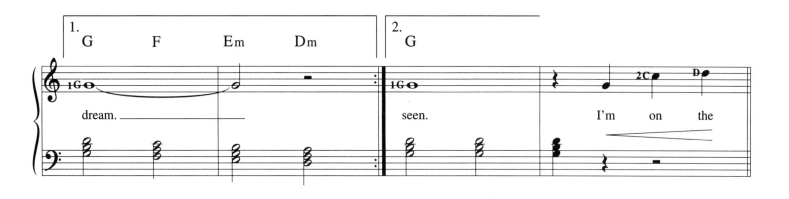

dream. _____ seen. I'm on the

CHORUS

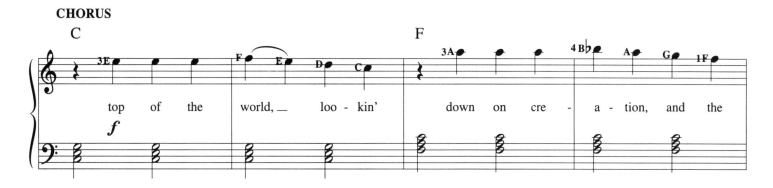

top of the world, __ loo - kin' down on cre - a - tion, and the

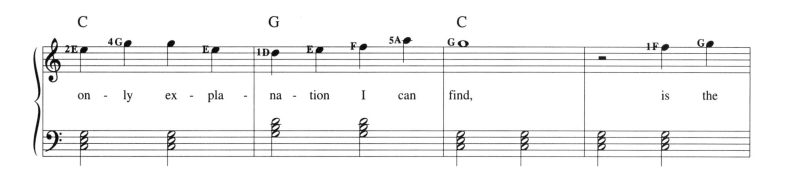

on - ly ex - pla - na - tion I can find, is the

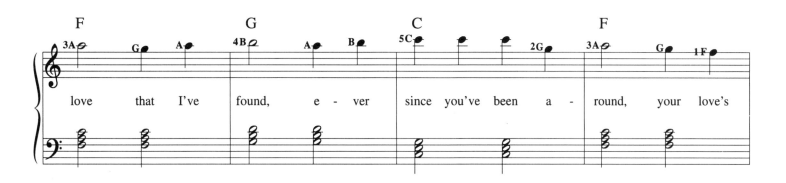

love that I've found, e - ver since you've been a - round, your love's

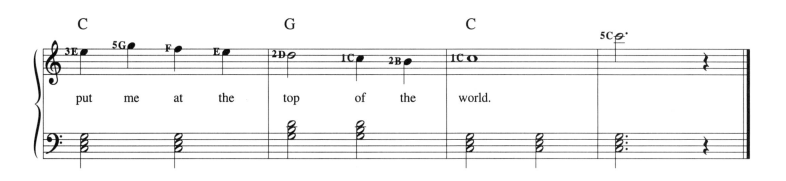

put me at the top of the world.

Wonderful Tonight

Words & Music by Eric Clapton

DA CAPO (D.C.) AL CODA
(From the beginning to CODA)

Repeat from the beginning of the piece until: **To Coda**.
From there jump to **Coda** (the final section of the piece),
and play through to the end.

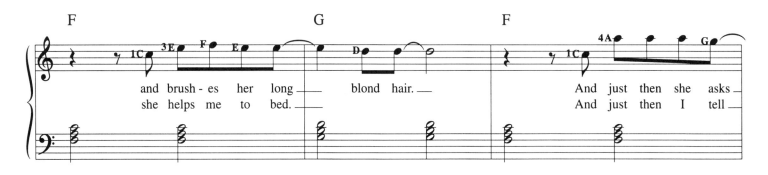

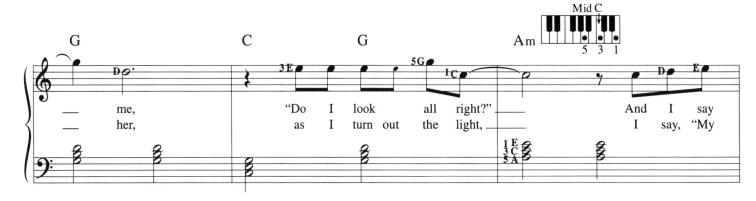

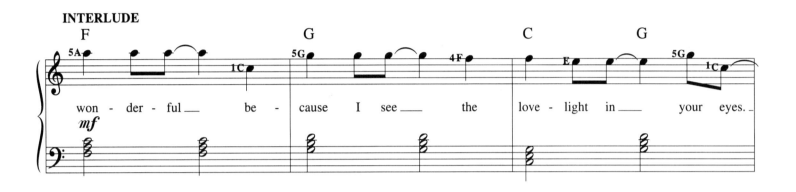

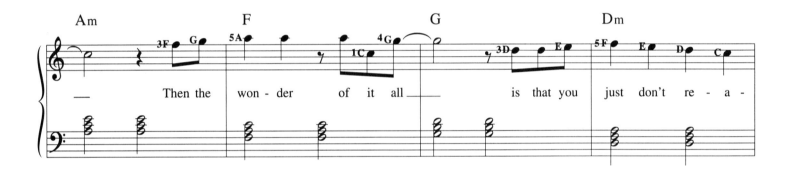

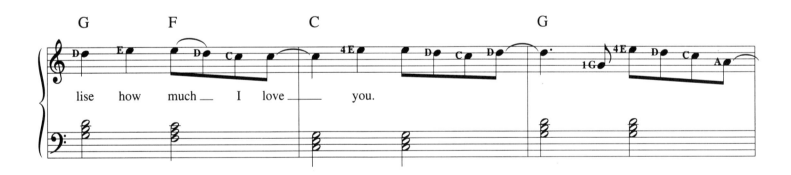

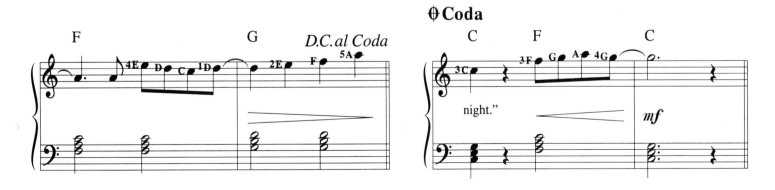

Super Trouper

Words & Music by Benny Andersson & Bjorn Ulvaeus

and it's gon-na be so dif - f'rent when I'm on the stage to - night. _____
ev - 'ry-thing will be so dif - f'rent when I'm on the stage to - night. _____ To - night the

CHORUS

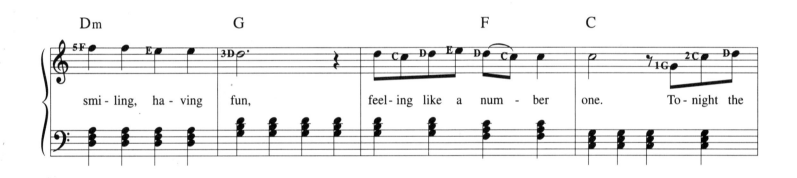

su - per trou - per lights are gon - na find _ me shi - ning like the sun,

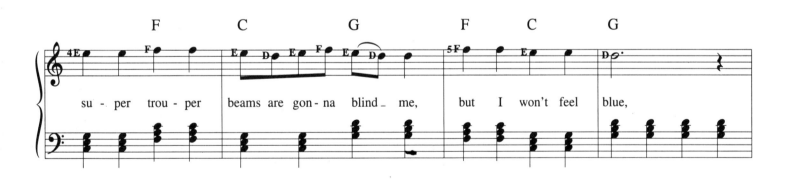

smi - ling, ha - ving fun, feel - ing like a num - ber one. To - night the

su - per trou - per beams are gon - na blind _ me, but I won't feel blue,

like I al - ways do, 'cause some - where in the crowd _ there's you.

TRIADS WITH BLACK NOTES

The following three new Major Triads require BLACK NOTES in the middle:-

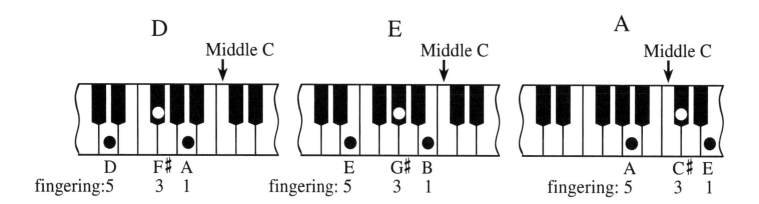

Compare these Major Triads with their Minor equivalents
(which you already know):- ·

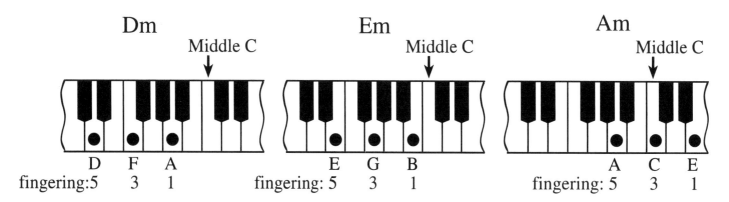

As usual, in the MINOR version of the above triads,
the middle note is **one semitone further to the left.**

THE SUSTAINING (DAMPER) PEDAL

This is the right hand pedal on your piano. This most useful device allows the note, or notes, to ring on after your fingers have left the keys. The sustaining pedal is especially useful when jumping from chord to chord in the left hand, as you are doing at the moment. LIFT the pedal as you play each new chord, then depress it again immediately afterwards and hold it down until the next harmony change. I have marked my suggested pedal changes like this:-

Ped.   change pedal (i.e. lift, then depress again).

✳   pedal off.

Scarborough Fair/Canticle

Arrangements & Original Counter Melody
by Paul Simon & Art Garfunkel

* RITENUTO. Slowing down gradually.

Sailing

Words & Music by Gavin Sutherland

The Lady In Red

Words & Music by Chris de Burgh

* ACCENT. (i.e. play louder)

KEY OF F (MAJOR)

Up to now you have been playing in the key of C MAJOR, which requires no sharps or flats. The next few pieces are written in the key of F MAJOR.
This key is derived from the **scale** of F (Major), which requires one flat: B♭ :-

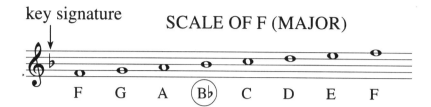

This B FLAT is indicated in the **key signature** at the beginning of every line of music, and you must remember to play every B note - **wherever it occurs on the keyboard** - as B FLAT.

NEW CHORDS

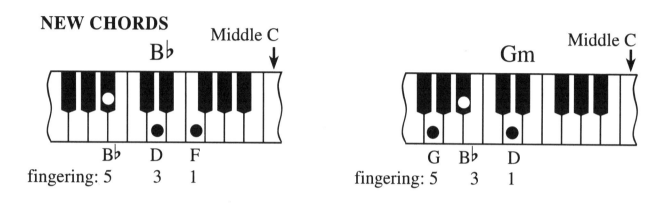

D.C. AL FINE (DA CAPO AL FINE) Repeat from the beginning of the piece, and continue until **Fine** (the end).

Guantanamera

Words by Jose Marti.
Music Adaptation by Hector Angulo and Pete Seeger

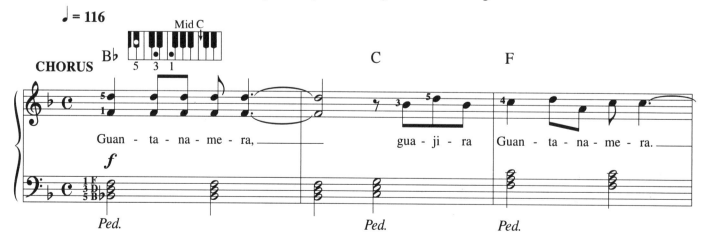

Without You

Words & Music by Peter Ham & Tom Evans

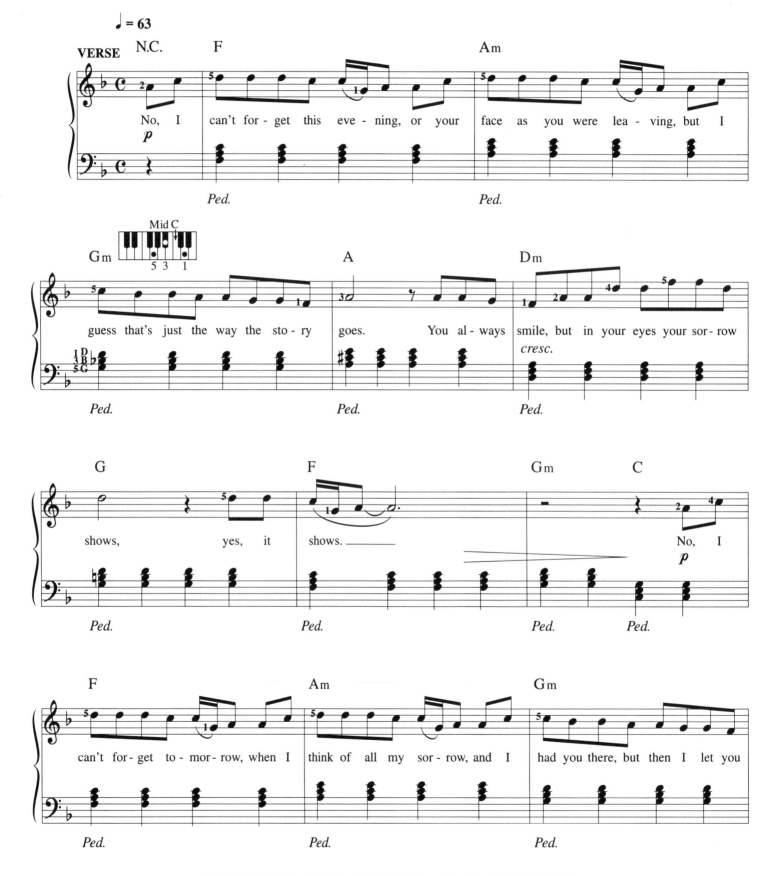

Wheels

Music by Norman Petty.
Words by Jimmy Torres & Richard Stephens

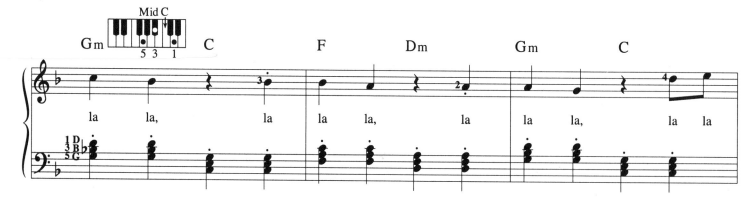

* SOSTENUTO. Hold this note down for its full length, or a little longer.

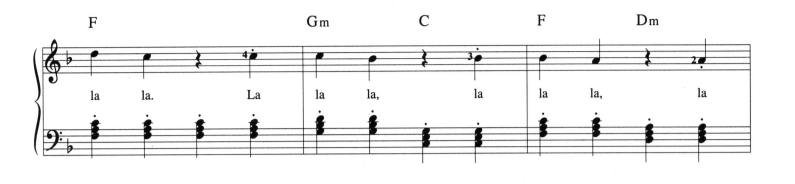

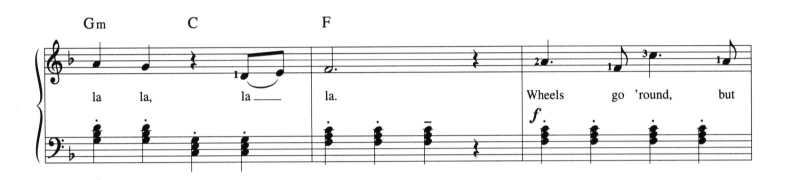

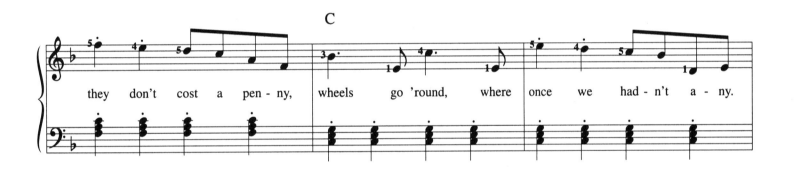

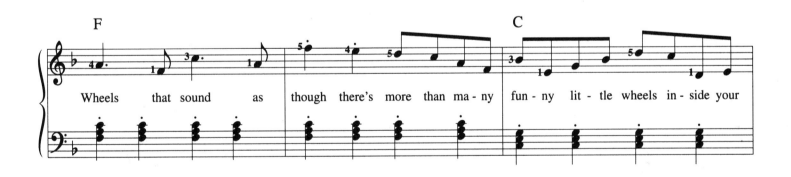

SPLITTING THE TRIAD

An interesting, and dynamic left hand accompaniment can often be achieved by playing parts of the triad separately:-

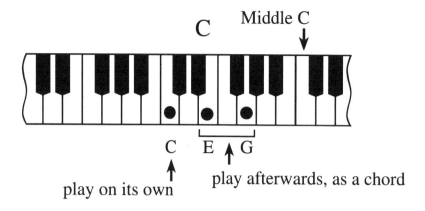

Examples:-

1. LOVE ME TENDER (p. 39)

Play a single note C on beat 1 and hold through beat 2. Add E and G together, as a chord, on beat 3, and hold all three notes down for the remainder of the bar. Repeat this pattern on the other triads.

2. ANNIVERSARY SONG (p. 42)

Play a single note E on beat 1, and double notes (G♯ and B) on beats 2 and 3.

In order to capture the 'lift' in this style, be sure to play the double notes STACCATO.

Love Me Tender

Words & Music by Elvis Presley & Vera Matson

* RITENUTO. Slowing down gradually.

There Goes My Everything

Words & Music by Dallas Frazier

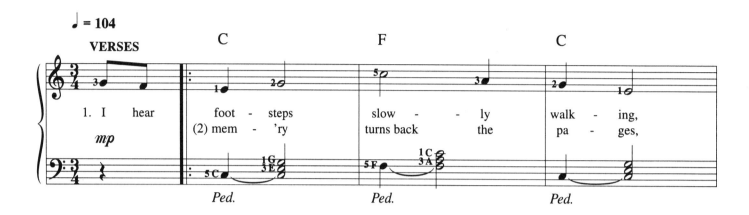

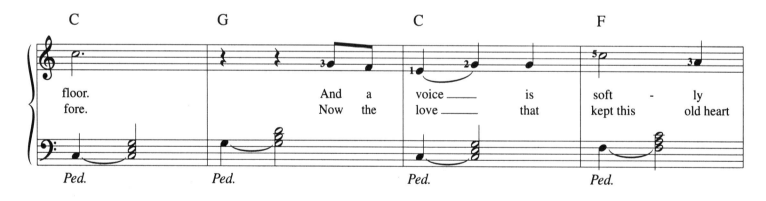

Anniversary Song

Words & Music by Al Jolson & Saul Chaplin

CHORD PYRAMIDS

In this attractive accompaniment style each note of the triad is played separately, then held down to form a sort of musical pyramid:-

GREEN GREEN GRASS OF HOME (p. 44)

Play note F on beat 1, and hold.
Add note A on beat 2, and hold.
Add note C on beat 3, and hold all three notes down for the remainder of the bar.
Repeat this pattern on the other triads.

Green, Green Grass Of Home

Words & Music by Curly Putman

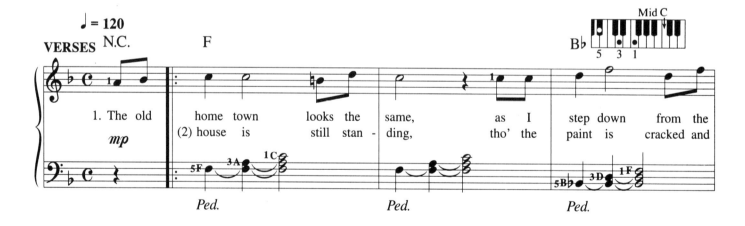

45

One Moment In Time

Words & Music by Albert Hammond & John Bettis

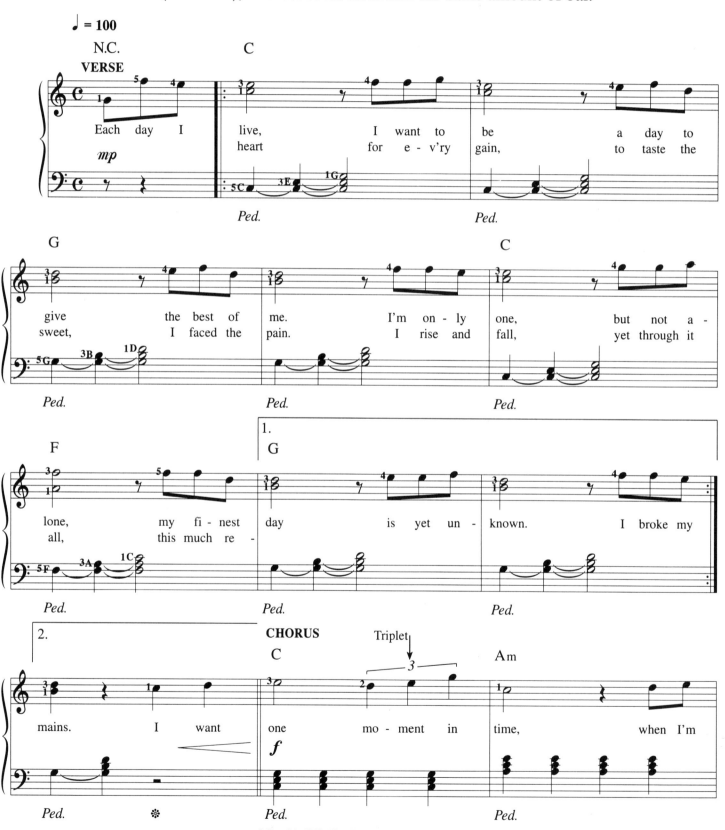

CHORD CHART

MAJOR

WRITTEN

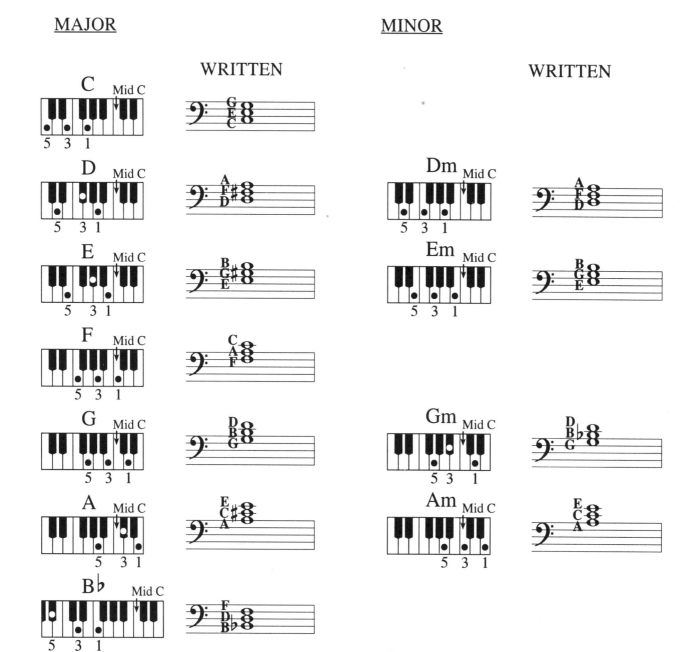

MINOR

WRITTEN

LEARNING THE WRITTEN NOTES (RIGHT HAND)

LINES

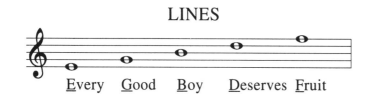

Every   Good   Boy   Deserves   Fruit

Two other important notes:-

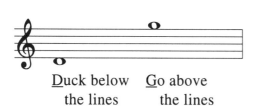

Duck below   Go above
the lines   the lines

SPACES

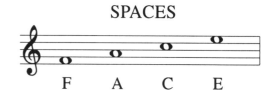

F   A   C   E

Beyond the stave, part lines, called
ledger lines are used:-

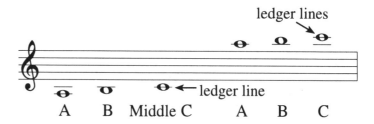

A   B   Middle C   A   B   C